"The Bravest Animals in the land
Are Captain Beaky and his band
That's Timid Toad, Reckless Rat,
Artful Owl and Batty Bat,
March through the woodland
Singing songs
That tell how they have righted wrongs. "

WRITTEN BY
JEREMY LLOYD

COMPILED BY
JONATHAN ROWLANDS

Captain Beaky and His Band Poems first published in
Captain Beaky Volume 1. 1976.
& Captain Beaky Volume 11. in 1981
by Chappell & Co London

This edition published October 2005 by Captain Beaky Ltd
www.captainbeaky.com

ISBN-10: 0-9551495-0-9

ISBN-13: 978-0-9551495-0-4

Permission to perform these poems on an amateur basis for stage and
concert may be obtained by emailing in the first instance to :-
Email: jonathan@captainbeaky.com

The publishers have used every reasonable effort to contact all copyright hold-
ers. Any errors that may have occured are inadvertent, and anyone who for
any reason has not been contacted is invited to email the publishers so that a
full acknowledgement may be made in subsequent editions of this work.

Design, Layout & Artwork by Gobion Rowlands, Red Redemption Ltd. web:
www.red-redemption.com, email: innovate@red-redemption.com
Printed in Great Britain by:

CONTENTS

* Captain Beaky and His Band Volume I CD
Features: The King's Singers, Jeremy Lloyd,
Keith Michell, Harry Secombe, Peter Sellers and Twiggy.

** Captain Beaky and His Band Volume II CD
Features: Petula Clark, Noel Edmonds,
Penelope Keith, The King's Singers, Jeremy Lloyd,
Keith Michell, Harry Secombe, Peter Skellern,
St. Paul's Choristers.

Both CDs are available through
www.captainbeaky.com

* As featured on Captain Beaky CD Volume I
** As featured on Captain Beaky CD Volume II

FOREWORD

A graveyard on a Summer's night the spectres dance in sheer delight and down a moonbeam slides a ginger cat in plimsolls and a paper hat.......

This was all I could find of a poem I wrote aged 12. Last year, aged about 40 something, I finished it. The poems had been written on the backs of envelopes, film scripts and in letters to friends over a period of years. When there appeared to be some interest in publishing them I found I was turning out old boxes of papers and writing to friends asking if I had by chance written them a poem, and if so, could I have it back. Keith Michell sent me some that I had completely forgotten writing.

Keith and I met when we were working together in Robert and Elizabeth at the Lyric. He being the leading man while I clanked on and off stage in Household Cavalry armour, as a dotty lover of his girlfriend's sister.

To pass the time I would scribble about the trials and tribulations of a lonely frog or penniless French mouse (both situations closely akin to my circumstances at the time) and Keith, an excellent artist with a great sense of humour, illustrated them. Our collaboration ceased abruptly when the Management allowed me to appear in a film, on condition I would be back for the evening performance. All my part required was that I should stand in front of a cannon and be shot. The explosion blew me across the studio, resulting in a lot of surgery and a 'get well slowly' card from my understudy.

I convalesced for part of the time in Jamaica and wrote Dilys the Dachshund on the back of an old record cover, which I received intact, minus Joe Loss's Greatest Hits, 12 years later.

The reason that I was suddenly trying to recover the poems was due to Lance Percival reading one on the radio show *"Start the Week"*. A publisher expressed interest, but I was told that at least 30 would be required to make up a book. About this time I got a call from Keith: could he read some on a TV show? Delighted, and please could I have them back?

Fate was obviously taking a hand, for a few days later I met Jonathan Rowlands, whom I had known in L.A. when I was writing *"Laugh In"*. I discovered that together with his partner, Hugh Murphy, his company had produced the Sir John Betjeman albums, of which he gave me copies. I was enchanted by Jim Parker's music, to which the poems were read, and showed him mine. In between writing *"Are You Being Served?"* Jim, Hugh, Jonathan and I worked together for a year with me writing new poems, Jonathan contacting the various artists, Jim composing the music and eventually Hugh, Jonathan and Jim producing the two albums.

I still find it hard to believe that these various characters have over the years come to life as a books, record albums, a no 2 hit single, several BBC TV shows, a 'West End Show', concerts and lately part of the National Youth Ballet performances but they have and I'm as delighted as they are.

- Jeremy Lloyd.

PRODUCER'S NOTES

We have loved being able to hear from all friends of Captain Beaky since going on line.

It has been these 'Beaky Freakies!', as they were originally known, who have over the years, through the medium of Books, LPs, Cassettes, CDs and now the Internet who have kept Captain Beaky and his little band of friends alive!

Since these Beaky aficionados have found us on the net we have received so many requests for their particular favourite Captain Beaky lyrics that we have decided to produce this book to satisfy the demand for the complete verses. For good measure we have added a little background on how the idea first took root.

I have loved the Captain Beaky Poems since I was first introduced to them one sunny afternoon in the mid 70's. Over a cappuccino in the Picasso, a popular hang-out in the Kings Road Chelsea, Jeremy Lloyd started reciting one of the many poems that as he says *"simply pop into his mind at night and when he wakes up there they are"*.

The poem was '*Down a Moonbeam Slides a Ginger Cat in Plimsolls and a Paper Hat*' and was followed swiftly by '*Teddy's Tea Time*'.

Publishing books of poetry is always a struggle so I decided that rather than the poems languishing in Jeremy's fertile mind they could reach a wider audience if they were linked into a musical format. Our first job was to interest Jim Parker (who had provided the wonderful backings for our Sir John Betjeman *'Banana Blush'* Album) to compose music especially for the poems.

Keith Michell who had kept many of the poems Jeremy had written whilst they were both in the play 'Robert and Elizabeth', then came on board as both performer and illustrator. Peter Sellers was the first artist in to the studio and we were away!

We toyed with many poem names eventually landing up with the generic title 'Captain Beaky' and then adding 'And His Band' so that it had a musical resonance.

When the albums and books were first released they sank without trace, but luck was on our side when Noel Edmonds heard Tony Blackburn play the record, grabbed it from his turntable – played it just once and the result was that an atomic scientist who was on secondment with the British Museum – upon hearing the show and recognising that Captain Beaky's *bête noire* Hissing Sid was not all that bad - wrote in proclaiming 'Hissing Sid Is Innocent Okay!'

The phrase tapped into the public psyche at the time and the result was - BBC Radio receiving 7,000 letter a week, Two Poetry Books on the best selling lists, a no 2 hit single, BBC TV Shows and a West End Musical. The best thing of course, is that the magic of Jeremy's writing of Captain Beaky and his little pals still lives on. Hurrah!

- Jonathan Rowlands

CAPTAIN BEAKY *

The bravest animals in the land
Are Captain Beaky and his band.
That's Timid Toad. Reckless Rat.
Artful Owl and Batty Bat.
March through the woodland
Singing songs
That tell how they have righted wrongs

Once Hissing Sid, an evil snake
Kept the woodland folk awake
In fear and trembling every night
In case he gave someone a bite.

Said Artful Owl, 'We'll lie in wait
And one of us will be the bait. ,
Said Captain Beaky, 'Have no fear
For I alone will volunteer.'

'No make it me,' said Reckless Rat,
'I'll stand there in my reckless hat
When Hissing Sid picks up my trail
I'll just lasso him with my tail.'

'Good idea,' said Timid Toad,
'We'll hide a long way down the road.
And when you've overcome resistance
We'll rush along to your assistance.'

Said Batty Bat, 'I've got a wheeze,
I'll fly and hide up in the trees.
If Hissing Sid should slither by,
I'll drop a boulder from the sky.'

Said Artful Owl, 'The idea's sound.
How will you lift it off the ground ?'
Poor Batty Bat just scratched his head,
'1 hadn't thought of that, he said.

Said Owl, 'The rest of us hold back,
There's only one that he'll attack.'
Said Timid Toad, '1 like your plan.'
'Good luck,' said Owl, 'For you're the man.'

So Timid Toad, his eyes a-popping,
Into the woodland night went hopping.
Captain Beaky waved his hand
Followed with. his trusted band
That's Artful Owl and Reckless Rat.
Above the trees flew Batty Bat.

'Stop, 'said Beaky, 'I hear squeaking.'
'It's Batty Bat,' said Owl, 'He's speaking
'It's all in code,' said Reckless Rat.
Said Owl, 'I'll just decipher that.'

A dash, a dot, two short, two long,
I rather hope I've got it wrong.
It reads, can clearly see the road.
Hissing Sid has captured Toad.'

'Quick men,' said Beaky, 'No delay,
You mustn't let him get away.'
And leaping off, said, 'Follow me,'
And ran head first into a tree

'Dot -dot -dot,' squeaked Batty Bat.
Said Beaky, 'Quick, decipher that.'
Cried Reckless Rat, 'Perhaps we're gaining
'No' said Owl 'He says it's raining.'

Oh how they ran to save poor Toad,
For they must find that Snake's abode.
Guided by old Batty Bat,
Dot - dot, go this way, Dash – go that.

Then Hissing Sid's lair they espied.
Were they too late ? Was he inside ?
Said Reckless Rat, '1'11 get a pole,
And stop him going down his hole.'

Then into sight the Snake came hopping,
Right past his hole, no sign of stopping
Said Reckless Rat, 'That's rather funny,
There's something jumping in his tummy.'

Said Captain Beaky, 'Well, I'm blowed,
Hissing Sid has swallowed Toad.'
And as the Snake hopped out of sight,
Off they chased into the night.

At last they found him, tired and dizzy
And pulled out Toad, who said,
'Where is he ? For left alone,
I felt quite sick and hopped into a hollow stick.'

Said Owl, 'A clever step to take,
You jumped into that Slippery Snake.'
'That was brave of Toad,' said Rat.
'That's just my sort of plan,' said Bat.

Said Captain Beaky to his men,
'We'll not see Hissing Sid again.'
And as they marched off down the road,
They sang in praise of Timid Toad.

Above them flew old Batty Bat,
With his wings stretched out quite flat.
Owl's idea, that clever fellah,
To have a flying umberella.

BLANCHE *

A baby owl, whose name was Blanche,
Perched bravely on a narrow branch,
And wondered whether she should try,
To jump off and attempt to fly.

She bravely counted up to ten,
And then she counted ten again.
She jumped !
She found she couldn't fly
And lay there looking at the sky.
'It's lucky that that branch,' said she,
Was on the ground, and not the tree.'

Then off she ran
And flapped her wings
And said 'These are most awkward things.
For though I skip and jump quite high,
I'm still no nearer to the sky,'

And falling down she gave a howl
And wished she'd never been an owl!
Finally her mother found her,
And put a great big wing around her,
Then said, 'Dear Blanche, don't be upset,
You haven't grown your feathers yet.'

THE BUMBLE BEE **

In his brown and yellow sweater,
Buzzing round the hollyhocks,
Flies a great big bumble bee
Wearing thick black woolly socks.
For bumble bees just live for pleasure
And never work a single day,
Oh what a lovely life of leisure
Just to buzz around and play.
In a big snapdragon snoozing
When the sun is just too hot
Then round the flowerbeds busy cruising
To find another comfy spot.
But there's a problem rather puzzling
And no one's solved the mystery.
Who knits those socks and big striped sweaters?
Can't be lazy bumble bees!

THE HAIRY NAIRN OF NAIRN

In the dreaded Castle Doom
In a locked up turret room,
Lived the Hairy Nairn of Nairn
Since he was a wee wee bairn.
Fed by ancient Miss MacFeeling,
Through a big hole in the ceiling.
Alas, he'd never learnt to eat
Except for great big chunks of meat.
And when an egg appeared he'd snatch it
Then sit on it and try to hatch it.
He'd pour his porridge on his head
And eat his porridge bowl instead,
And when he got a pair of kippers
He made them into carpet slippers.
Until one Christmas, Miss MacFeeling
Put a haggis through the ceiling.
Unaccustomed to such sights
He tried to play it like the pipes.
Alas, of course, no sound emitted
And with a roar of rage he bit it,
And then, the Hairy Nairn of Nairn,
Locked up since he was a bairn,
Smiled a hairy smile and said,
'No more porridge on my head.
No more great big chunks of meat,
No more kippers on my feet,
No more eggs I'll try to hatch,
No more food I'll have to snatch.'
And with a big contented sigh,
Said, 'I'll eat the bagpipes till I die!'

CYRIL THE CENTIPEDE

Cyril. the centipede
Loved playing games,
And his favourite one was football.
And when he played goal
With nine fleas and a mole
Nothing got past him at all.
They played spiders and newts
But his one hundred boots
Gave his team very little to do
And the fleas would get bored,
The mole never scored
And the crowd would just stand there and boo.

'Til one awful day the crowd stayed away
And no fans for either side came,
But all said and done
When it's none none none none,
It's really not much of a game.
Then Cyril the centipede
Hurt his back leg
The hundre'th one down on the right
So he used a small stick
And went 99 click,
Now I'm happy to say it's all right,
But he doesn't play goal
Any more - he's retired
Unbeaten, for nobody scored.
Now he just referees
For the spiders and fleas.
And even the mole
Has just scored.

DENNIS THE DORMOUSE *

Young Dennis the dormouse
Was frightfully frail
And hated to hear a hinge squeak.
And should a door slam at the height of a gale
He'd retire to his bed for a week

A rattly old chain
Would give him a jolt
And he'd get wobbly knees and go pale.
And even the sound of a softly drawn bolt
Made him cover his ears with his tail.

So he searched round the house
For a small can of oil
And a couple of sticks and some twine
Which he made into stilts with much labour and toil.
Now Dennis the dormouse is fine.

For he's oiled the locks
Of each room in the house,
All the bolts and the hinges as well.
And everything now is as quiet as a mouse,
What a pity he can't reach the bell.

DESMOND THE DUCK *

With foxes abroad
Few ducks can afford
To leave a new egg in a nest,
And should they do so
They usually go
For it's duck eggs that foxes like best.
And Desmond the duck
Had awfully bad luck,
Even before he was born,
Whilst still in his egg
With his nose round his leg
A fox came and took him at dawn.
Unaware of his plight
And the subsequent flight
Of the fox with the egg he had snatched,
Desmond tapped on his shell
And let out a yell .
For he thought it was time he was hatched.
The fox stopped with surprise,
And in front of his eyes
A small beak appeared through a crack,
Then a head, then a leg
Appeared from the egg
Then Desmond, who fell on his back.
'Look Mummy,' he said,
'There's a bump on my head,
But I couldn't wait there any longer,
And now I've been born,
Will you please keep me warm,
And take care of me till I grow stronger.'

The fox shook his head,
'I'm sorry: he said,
'But alas there's no going back.
I'm a fox, you're a duck,
That's right out of luck,
And I'm taking you home for a snack.'
Said Desmond, 'All right,
I could do with a bite,
But first could you answer my question.
What are these on my back?
And why can't you quack?'
Said the fox, 'You've upset my digestion.
I'll take you back home,
My heart isn't stone,
And life as a duck can be fun.
On the rivers and lakes
You can play ducks and drakes,
Quite often I've wished I was one.'
Said Desmond, 'Hooray,
What fun, come and play
Any time that you're passing and bored.'
Said the fox with a smile,
'It'll be a long while,
For foxes are always abroad.'

ELOISE THE SILKWORM

There was a lady silkworm,
Whose name was Eloise,
Whose sister Sybil Silkworm,
Was very hard to please.
Eloise had found at last,
A worm she could adore,
And was busy weaving silken threads
For her bottom drawer.
Alas, he was a common worm,
And Sybil disapproved,
And with such common neighbours,
It was clearly time they moved.
But Eloise was adamant,
She said, 'I love dear Ern,
And though it is a common name,
He's just my kind of worm.
And though he lives up on the common,
Under common ground,
Nothing that you say or do,
Will stop his common round.'

THE SPIDER KING

The absent-minded Spider King,
Couldn't quite do anything,
And thro' his web the flies all flew,
For he'd forget to use the glue.
And when he did, he wasn't clever
He'd get his legs all stuck together,
And falling like a bouncing ball
He'd end up sticking to the wall,
And mutter with exasperation,
'Another sticky situation.'
What's the fun of being King,
When you can't do anything?

CLAUDE THE CRAB

Claude an anxious looking crab,
Whose eyes stood out on stalks,
Would stroll about beneath the sea,
On long and lonely walks.
He often tried to reach the beach
Where other crabs reside.
But just when it was in his reach
He'd be swept back by the tide.
Then with six legs he'd scratch his head
And sigh, 'Oh dearie me.
I'm fed up with my deep sea bed,
I'd love to leave the sea.'
And so the weeks and months went by
For poor old anxious Claude,
Without a glimpse of sun or sky.
My word he did get bored.
Until one day a fishing boat
Cast anchor overhead
And dropped a tasty bit of bait
Which fell to the sea bed.
And as it was his breakfast time
And hung within his reach
He tugged and went up with the line
As they headed for the beach.
And Claude who'd never been ashore
Yelled, 'Hang on, wait for me.'
And so they did, and what is more,
They took him home for tea.

DILYS THE DACHSHUND *

Dilys the dachshund hated snow,
Because her middle was so low.
And once when it was really snowing
She only had her tail showing.
So in her woolly winter clothes
She practised walking on her toes,
And with an anxious little grin
Went for a stroll, with stomach in,
And in the middle of her walk
Was spotted by a talent hawk.
Who cried, as soon as he had seen her,
He knew she'd make a ballerina.
He'd christen her Dilys Barkover
One day she'd dance with Rudi Rover.
Dilys thrilled at thoughts of fame
Could hardly wait to change her name,
And quickly had the contract signed
Before the hawk could change his mind.
She rushed back home to break the news
And bought some tiny ballet shoes.

She went to London on the train.
In search of fortune and acclaim,
And after weeks of leaps and bounds
And back legs stretch with taller hounds,
Dilys got a lucky break
To play a cygnet in Swan Lake.

On the CD
(*'Who is that new girl?'*
'She's good! isn't she Rudy')

She danced so well, with grace and speed,
Some said, she should have got the lead.
And when she did a paw de deux
Everyone applauded her.
'Til Dilys, heady with success
Performed impromptu arabesques
Underneath the royal box,
Where sat the Prince, a handsome fox.
Then jumping up on pointed toes
She spun away across the snow.
The Prince leapt forward with surprise
And raised some glasses to his eyes,
For Dilys, spinning like a top
Had spun so far she couldn't stop.
Musicians paused and frowned uncertain,
Stage hounds whispered 'drop the curtain',
But wait, the Prince stood up and clapped
And then, her shoe elastic snapped. Disaster!
As high up in the air there flew
A tiny, silken ballet shoe.
Up towards the royal box,
Where stood the Prince, the handsome fox,
He caught it in mid air,
Still warm,
Kissed it,
And a star was born.

And so dear dachshunds be of cheer,
It may well snow for you next year.

JOCK THE FLEA **

Jock a Scottish Circus flea,
Could jump a height of one foot three.
And in his kilt, both short and brief
Could bend a mouse hair in his teeth.
He used to get his best applause
As in his silver spangled drawers
And rubber shoes, lest be should slip,
He'd lift a great big orange pip.
Alas, ambition drove to hard
He tried to lift a playing card.
And with assistance from a friend
He got it to stand, up on end.
Now sad to say, poor Jock is dead.
The ace of spades fell on his head.
That fatal card!

DEAD MATCHES

Seven dead matches on the floor
And in an ashtray are two more,
And on the scene young P.C. Swan,
Red haired and anxious to get on,
A match for any sort of crime,
But on this case had little time.
The two detectives on their way,
Detective-sergeants, Bryant and May,
Had a flair for finding clues
And there was little time to lose.
So P.C. Swan with puzzled frown
Searched to find who'd struck them down,
And taking off his helmet said,
'Who done this,' and scratched his head.
A fatal move, as it transpired,
Young P.C. Swan at once expired.
And no one yet has solved the crime,
Bryant and May might, given time,
Of seven dead matches on the floor
And in an ashtray are three more.

GEORGE THE GIRAFFE

Young George the giraffe
Used to wear a big scarf
And in winter time donned a warm coat.
For he lived in a zoo
And had twice caught the flu,
And often he had a sore throat.
So far from his home
He'd stand there alone.
And dream of the African plain,
Where he'd lived as a lad
With his mum and his dad
And he wished he could see them again.
For life in a zoo
When you're prone to the flu
And you've got the world's longest sore throat
Despite thick pyjamas
And lots of bananas,
Makes you want to get on the next boat.
So next time you go to the zoo
And they show
Every animal there except one,
A lonely giraffe, in a coat and a scarf,
It means George has escaped to the sun.

FRED THE GRASSHOPPER

A young grasshopper
Whose name was Fred,
Was told by his mother
To go to bed.
But the night was hot,
He couldn't sleep,
So out of the window, with a leap
To jump about and stretch his knees
Till catching cold, he gave a sneeze.
Leaping back he banged his nut,
His sneeze had blown the window shut!

THE SNAIL *

Search round in the garden,
You're bound to find a snail.
Perhaps you've always wondered why
They leave a sticky trail?
Some people think it's left for friends
To show which way they're going.
Well, that's not the reason that
A snail leaves a trail showing.
The answer's plain. They cannot see
An inch beyond their noses,
Or recognize the rockery
From a bed of roses.
And snails have no memory
Which gets them in a mess.
That's why they wear their houses,
To remember their address.
And so they leave a sticky trail,
Strange as it may seem.
Not to show the way they've gone,
It's to remind them where they've been.

HAROLD THE FROG *

Harold a rather lonely frog,
With spotted, manly chest,
Lived in a wet and squelchy bog
And always looked depressed.
He couldn't get a froggy date,
Although he'd try each night
But when he'd squelch' behind a girl
She'd just leap off in fright.
A wallflower at the local hop
He'd dance 'till dawn alone,
Quick, quick, quick, slow, quick
Plop, plop, plop.
Then squelch his way back home.
Reflecting in his private pool
On his unhappy fate,
He wondered why on earth it was
He couldn't get a date
His friends all knew the reason why,
But friends don't like to tell
A frog who's got and doesn't know;
A wet and boggy smell!

HERBERT THE HEDGEHOG *

Young Herbert the hedgehog
Lived on a hill and his home
Had a wonderful view
Of swans in a lake
Who loved eating cake
That picnickers quite often threw.
And on hot summer days
Young Herbert would gaze
At the children down there having fun,
For he loved watching kites
And some flew to great heights
And often he wished he had one.
And when the days ended
And people packed up all their baskets
To wend their way home,
Young Herbert would sigh and wave them good-bye
For it's not much fun living alone.
But he had things to do
For spoiling the view,
Was the litter, left by one and all.
So Herbert would climb
To the top of his hill and curl himself up into a ball,
Then down he would rush
Like a little brown brush
And the paper would stick on his spikes.
Then he'd dig with his feet
A hole to be neat
For it's litter a hedgehog dislikes,
So next time you picnic
Perhaps by a lake
And you think there's a wonderful view,
Remember a hedgehog who worked very hard
To tidy the place up for you.

THE GINGER CAT *

A graveyard on a summer's night,
The spectres dance in sheer delight,
And down a moonbeam slides a ginger cat
In plimsolls and a paper hat.

'I'm dead,' he cried, 'My name was Ben,
I had nine lives and just spent ten,
And now I am a ghostly cat,
In plimsolls and a paper hat.'

'Tell us Ben,' the spectres cried,
'The different ways in which you died.'
'Gather round me then,' said Ben,
'And I'll tell you where, and when.'

'The first time I fell down the well,
No one near to hear me yell'
'How did you escape,' they said,
'When you'd been given up for dead?'

'I found a bucket,' said the cat,
'And so I went to sleep in that.
And then a local farmer's daughter
Pulled it up to get some water.
Lucky to escape from that,
In plimsolls and a paper hat.'

'The second time, still very clear,
I found a fish head on the pier,
And took it in my mouth with glee,
Then someone threw it in the sea.
They were using it as bait,
I really thought I'd met my fate.'
'How did you escape,' they said,
'When you'd been given up for dead?

'I met a catfish in the sea,
Who rather liked the look of me,
And pulled me by my ginger tail
To the shore, all cold and pale.
Lucky to escape from that,
In plimsolls and a paper hat.'

'The third time nearly was my end,
Upon a roof top with a friend
I slipped right down a chimney pot
And down towards my doom, I shot.'
'How did you escape,' they said,
'When you'd been given up for dead?'

'But for the soot, I would have died.
They had a chimney sweep inside
And as his brush swept up the flue
Back I popped as good as new.
Lucky to escape from that!
In plimsolls and a paper hat.'

'The fourth time, in a castle cellar
I met a rat, enormous fellah.
Each eye redder than a ruby
Was I frightened? Wouldn't you be?'
'How did you escape,' they said,
'When you'd been given up for dead?'

'I hid behind a wooden log,
And howled and barked just like a dog.
Oh my, you should have seen him run
I chased him half a mile for fun.
He never knew I was a cat
In plimsolls and a paper hat.'

'The fifth time, on an evening stroll,
I came across a rabbit hole.
And being curious, popped inside
And sitting there a fox. I spied.'
'How did you escape,' they said,
'When you'd been given up for dead?'

'I said, dear Fox I've just come here,
To warn you that the hunt is near.'
'Thank you Cat,' the fox replied,
'But for you, I might have died.
I have a friend, for life, a cat
In plimsolls and a paper hat.'

'The sixth time was on Beachy Head,
Sleeping on a disused bed.
When I awoke, I went quite stiff
For it was falling o'er the cliff.'
'How did you escape,' they said,
'When you'd been given up for dead?'

'I got four corners of a sheet
And held on with my hands and feet
And as the cliff was out of reach
I parachuted to the beach.
Lucky to escape from that,
In plimsolls and a paper hat.'

'The seventh time was in a house,
The owner hoped I'd catch a mouse.
He said, that's all I get to eat
Alas there, were no mice to meet.'
'How did you escape,' they said,
'When you'd been given up for dead?'

'The doors were locked, I nearly died,
Then a paint pot I espied,
Jumped in his bedroom, painted white,
He yelled and ran into the night.
Lucky to escape from that
In plimsolls and a paper hat.'

'Eight and nine lives lost together,
In a nasty bout of weather.
For in the hail and snow and rain
I was swept off down a drain.'
'How did you escape,' they said,
'When you'd been given up for dead?'

'Lost down below a London street,
A great big turtle did I meet.
Been in the drains since he was small
And knew his way around them all.
Lucky to escape from that,
In plimsolls and a paper hat.'

'And now we come to number ten,
Which really was the end of Ben.
I caught the Cat Flu, how, don't ask it,
And died whilst sleeping in my basket.'

'Now all my lives have gone,' he said,
'Alas, at last I'm really dead.'
Then up the moonbeam climbed the cat
In plimsolls and a paper hat.

RONALD THE RAT *

Ronald Rat looks quite a swell
And lives in London docks,
He wears a battered bowler hat,
And knee-length yellow socks.
And once he wore a driving glove,
Just to wave to friends,
But alas, he has no car,
For Ronald just pretends.
He's not a millionaire at all,
Just a dockside rat,
But you'd never guess,
When he wears his glove,
And socks and bowler hat.

WILFRED THE WEASEL *

The church bell strikes
The hour of noon,
In the village on the hill,
And across the fields and meadows,
Echoes its thin silver note,
To the ears of Wilfred Weasel,
Seated at his artist's easel,
As he waits for inspiration,
In his floppy hat and coat,
Brush in hand and palette ready,
As he's been since half past eight,
Empty canvas indicating
Inspiration's sleeping late.
But though the bell notes fade forever,
Conjured up and left behind,
In a blinding flash
A vision clear as crystal in his mind.
With all the style of Leonardo
And daring use of green and blue
Deft strokes tell a moving story,
'Gone to lunch and back at two.'

PEG THE BABY HEN

A baby hen, whose name was Peg,
Said, 'Mummy, can I lay an egg?
I wish you'd show me what to do,
Then I could help you with a few.'
Her mother smiled, and shook her head.
'You're far too young for that,' she said,

'But do the things that you've been taught,
And think a nice round eggy thought
And one day, it will come to pass,
An egg will pop out on the grass.'

THELMA THE THRUSH

Thelma the thrush
Made her home in a train.
Just under the engine
To keep out the rain.
Along came the driver
Who said, 'Oh my word.
I can't move the train
Or I'll frighten the bird.'
Along came the head
Of the railway track,
Who said to the driver,
'I'll give you the sack.
Drive off at once,
You're already late.'
'Not me,' said the driver,
'Nor me,' said his mate,
And smiled down at Thelma
Who looked quite dismayed,
For while they'd been talking
Four eggs had been laid.
'Well that's it.' said the
Head of the railway track.
'You can't drive off now
Or the eggs will all crack.
I'd best phone the station,
But what shall I say?'
Said the driver, 'The truth,
Uneggspected delay.'

NORMAN THE ZEBRA

Norman, a zebra at the zoo,
Escaped and ran to Waterloo
And caused a lot of consternation,
In the rush-hour, at the station.
He had an awful lot of fun
Chasing folk on Platform 1,
And then he ran to Regent's Park
And hid there until it was dark,
And thought of his keeper Mr Prout,
How cross he'd be, that he'd got out.
So he tiptoed to the big zoo gate
And found he'd got there just too late.
Poor Norman had a little weep
And lay down in the road to sleep
And woke up early from his rest,
With people walking on his chest.
And someone said, 'I think that's new,
A zebra crossing near the zoo.'
And with a snort of indignation,
Regretting leaving for the station,
He cried, 'I've had enough of that,
How dare you use me as a mat.
I'm going straight home to the zoo.'
He was just in time for breakfast too.

JACQUES A PENNILESS FRENCH MOUSE *

A penniless French mouse called Jacques,
In beret, boots and belted mac,
Strode idly down an empty drain
Protected 'gainst the wind and rain,
When from a grating in the street
A cigarette fell at his feet,
And in surprise, he cried:
'Mon Dieu!
It is my favourite brand,
Disque Bleu.
Ma foi, these are très fort,' he said.
Inhaling deep, the end glowed red.
A smell, he thought, was just le drain,
Was gas escaping from le main.
Le grande explosion, au r'voir Jacques,
In beret, boots and belted mac.
And now he has gone
To the great mousehole in the sky,
Where mountains of le cheese
Stretch away as far as the eye can see.
'Excusez-moi, monsieur. . .'
'Oui?'
'Which way to le Roquefort, s'il vous plaît?'

NATHANIEL GNAT *

The statue is tiny
I doubt that you'd see it
But it's no less important for that:
It's an insect resplendent
In top hat and tails
And inscribed to 'Nathaniel Gnat'.
Look at his tile
Ain't it got style
Butchers the weasel and stoat,
That's cockney for hat and his coat
And all that,
Which accounts for the smile on his boat.
He departed this world
Umbrella well furled
When his spats tangled up with some trees.
A strange way to die
For a gnat who could tie
A cravat with such elegant ease.
Some witnesses said
Though he fell on his head
He could have been saved by his hat,
But smart to the last
Although falling fast
He removed it in case it went flat.
Now thanks to his style
And that brave marble smile
We find, when with clothes we're impressed,
That we tend to apply,
And now you know why,
The expression 'He's nattily' dressed'.

At the recording of the BBC's "Captain Beaky's World of Words and Music" (Left to right: Noel Edmonds, Keith Michell, Penelope Keith, Jeremy Lloyd and Peter Skellern)

Keith Michell, Penelope Keith, Jeremy Lloyd and Jonathan Rowlands cutting the cake at the Chappell Golden Book Award

The Beaky Team
(Left to right: Jonathan, Keith, Jeremy, Jim and Hugh)

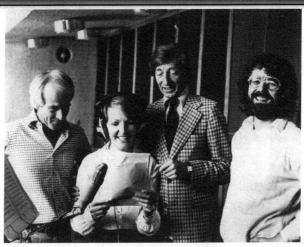

In the Studio at Producer's Workshop recording
(Left to right: Jim, Penelope, Jeremy and Jonathan)

MY BEST FRIEND *

Save for the humming of the bees
And raindrops falling thro' the trees,
The wood was silent as a grave
Whilst shafts of sunlight made a brave
Attempt to pierce the velvet gloom
As lonely as an empty room.
Alone was I, but not afraid,
The friend I'd been with must have strayed,
For tho' I called, no answer came
And so I played a splendid game
In the bracken wet and thick
With my favourite walking stick.
And then, a voice called out quite near:
'So there you are, old chap, come here.'
And sitting there, upon a log
Was my best friend, who said: 'Good dog.'

THE HAGGIS SEASON *

The haggis season has begun.
All over Scotland every gun
Is taken down with loving care,
Though some prefer the haggis snare
For haggis are a wily lot,
That's why they are so seldom shot.
Then hidden in the Highland heather
Great hairy clansmen crouch together,
And having laid the haggis bait
(A lifelike haggis on a plate),
One cries out loudly 'There the noo !'
Which means a haggis is in view.
It's flying upside down and low
The guns all fire but they're too slow.
For though it's rather old and fat
They're awful hard to hit like that!
And as it flies off in the mists,
Great hairy clansmen shake their fists
And scream their curses to the crags
Then stamp on empty haggis bags.
And so the haggis gets away to live
Until next Hogmanay.
And that's the reason it's so rare,
This strange traditional Scottish fare.

Captain Beaky For P.M.

Said Captain Beaky to his Band
'What's happened to the Nation?'
'All I seem to hear about'
'Are strikes and more inflation'
'I heard that too', said Timid Toad
'It didn't bother me although I often'
'Get inflated when I've had my tea'

'That's typical', said Artful Owl
'Of those who just don't care'
'It's up to us to pull our weight'
'And try and do our share'
Said Captain Beaky, 'I agree'
'Now here's a question men'
'Are we keen on who's in charge'
'Up at Number 10?'

Said Reckless Rat, 'it seems to me'
'In the interest of the Nation'
'We really ought to keep them there'
'To save redecoration'
Said Captain Beaky, 'good point Rat'
'But to be a politician'
'Needs lots of brains, so hands up those
who fancy the position'

Said Batty Bat, 'I'd quite like that'
Said Owl, 'we hadn't planned'
'On our PM hanging upside down
from an umbrella stand'

'If I were there', said Timid Toad
'I'd just give lots of teas'
'And instead of chocolate biscuits'
'I'd hand out O.B.E.s

'I'd like the post', said Captain Beaky
'In fact I'm rather keen'
'Not to run the Country though'
Just to meet the Queen'
'I'd stroll up to the Palace'
'To have a general chat'
'And when I'd leave they'd all salute'
'My word I would like that'

'The trouble is the papers'
Said Owl, 'if they'd all strike'
'We'd never know how bad things were'
'Or what we didn't like'
'Let's leave the Cabinet alone'
'Don't even lift the lid'
'You're right', said Captain Beaky
'We might find Hissing Sid'

So they didn't go to Number 10
They stayed there in the Wood
Righting wrongs, singing songs
And trying to do good
Like most of us they find it hard
To change the situation
But after all it does no harm
To have a conversation.

The Trial of Hissing Sid **

Today's a special day
For Captain Beaky and his Band
Since Hissing Sid's been brought to trial
And in the dock he stands
Presiding is Lord Justice Pig
Who bangs his gavel twice
'Order!' cried the Clerk,
Said Batty Bat, 'I'll have an ice'

'A good idea' said Timid Toad
'Make mine a lemon tea'
'Just one more word,' said Justice Pig
'And you'll do one to three'
'I won't have talking in my court'
'In law it's called contempt'
Said Artful Owl, 'as prosecution'
'I trust I'll be exempt'

Now Captain Beaky and his band
That's Rat, Bat, Toad and me
Apprehended Hissing Sid
Whilst doing villainy
Said Justice Pig, 'be more precise'
'What dark deed did he do?'
Said Batty Bat, 'before you sat'
'He wiped your seat with glue'
Said Justice Pig, 'It's not your turn'
'Your outburst I've deleted'
(snort) 'But as I've tried to get up twice'
'The Court will all stay seated

Said Q.C. Crow, 'I must object'
'To rabbits on the Jury'
'The way this case is going on ,
'My client's stiff with fury'
'What's wrong with rabbits Owl?' said Bat
'They look alright to me'
Said Beaky, 'there were 12 just now'
'And now there's 23'
'24!' cried Justice Pig,
'There's one more by my chair'
Said Q.C. Crow, 'there's little doubt'
'This trial is most unfair'

'And how can all these rabbits'
'Just arrived know good from bad?'
'They can't of course,' said Justice Pig
'Now hands up this one's dad'
'I f-fear we've lost the case,' said Toad
Sighed Beaky, 'sad but true'
Said Owl, 'there's one charge that will stick'
Cried Beaky, 'right, the glue'

Then they saw the empty dock
'He's gone,' cried Reckless Rat
'And so has my best overcoat'
'And where's my reckless hat?'
Said Beaky, 'he's disguised himself'
'It's up to us to find him'
And as he leapt off through the woods
His band were close behind him
But though they searched both high and low
And all points in between
Not a sign of Hissing Sid in
Hat and coat was seen

Said Bat, 'I'll fly up in the sky'
'And see if I can spot him'
Said Timid Toad, 'I'll hold my breath'
'And breathe out when you've got him'
'The weather's turning warm,' said Owl
'Who needs a hat and coat'
'We could spend the afternoon'
'All happily afloat'
'Good idea,' said Reckless Rat
'Right ho,' said Captain Beaky
'We'll climb aboard my biscuit tin'
'The H.M.S. Most Leaky'

And as they sailed off down the Thames,
Bat searched with all his might
Until he signalled 'S.O.S.'
Which means, Snake Out Of Sight
Said Beaky, 'shouldn't Toad be green?'
'I fear he's turning blue'
'He hasn't let his breath out yet'
Cried Rat, 'what shall we do?'
Said Owl, 'just pass the pepper pot'
'It's sure to make him sneeze'
'Apart from which, the wind's just dropped'
'We need the extra breeze'
Uh-uh-uh-uh-chew!

And guess who watched them disappear
From a dark hole where he hid
With beady eyes 'neath stolen hat,
You're right - yes, Hissing Sid.

ENRICO THE CANARY **

Enrico the Canary
Had a voice magnificente
Singing opera all day long
Despite an accidente
In which he sadly lost a leg-a
A cat he met was quicker
So now he has a wooden one
Made of a small matchstick-a

But the lady he belonga to
Got very very old-a
And then she died so he was sent
To a pet shop to get sold-a
One day a rich man passing by
Heard Enrico singing Verdi
And stopping goes into the shop
And says, 'I buy the birdie'.

And then he look and look again
And says, 'what's thees I see?
That bird has got a wooden leg,
So it's no good to me'
Said Enrico, 'Stop! Before you go,
Though my leg's tied on with string-a
What are you looking for my friend
A dancer, or a singer?'

BROWSER LONG THE BOOKWORM **

Browser Long the bookworm
met a worm called Mabel
Boring through a dictionary
on a library table.
Said Browser Long, ''Ello, 'ello,
I like the way you look.'
'Oh good,' said Mabel, 'Come to T,
you'll find me in the book'

'Call round at three on Tuesday next,
we'll have a celebration'
'I'll shop for clothes at C&A,
then meet you at the station.'
Browser Long could hardly wait
until next Tuesday came
Despite the fact he hadn't asked
his lady friend's last name.

He ate his way through all the A's,
and shortly after starting,
Caught B for Boat and sailed the C's
arriving at departing,
Then dined on Doughnuts, Dates and Duck
as fast as one can read,
Then went right through from Drink to Drunk
at full Dictation speed

Eating E for Energy
he jumped the first Express
Then rode on R for Railway
down the letter S
There was Mabel at the Station,
Standing with her Shopping.
Alas it was a Straight-through train
and not one that was Stopping.

So Browser Long jumped from the train,
an F for Foolish action,
Now Mabel visits him each day
as he lies in T for Traction.
Her last name's not important now,
he's no longer keen
Since he's found she lives by accident
at the top of page 13.

DOTTY THE CUCKOO **

Dotty, a short-sighted Cuckoo
Laid an egg in a discarded hat
A silly mistake, but easy to make
When your eyesight's as dodgy as that

An elderly tramp passing by, saw it
And said, 'it's your lucky day Fred'
'A discarded hat, I think I'll have that'
'It's just the right size for my head'

Three weeks, night and day, Fred wore it
'Til one day in the Pub with a beer
The hat rose, then fell, and Fred with a yell
Said,' there's summat just nibbled my ear.'

An old lady fainted, the barman went white
As a small yellow beak came in view
And a purple-nosed Colonel said,
'Heavens I'm tight!'
'And it's only a quarter to two.'

The hat was removed to reveal a small bird
Cried the Landlord, 'quick phone the reporters'
Said the bird, 'when you do,
give my name and size too'
'Harrods, Six and three quarters.'

WENDELL THE WORM **

Wendell the Worm used to wriggle and squirm
For sunburn had made his nose itch
So he got a small mirror to have a close look
But he couldn't tell which end was which
So he broke off a daisy and made a small hat
sighing life as a worm's pretty rotten
Then he looked in the mirror and said 'look at that'
I'm wearing a hat on my bottom.
I'll just see my doctor, he's down the next hole
When he came out he looked rather pale
For he'd found he'd described all his symptoms at length
To the non-speaking end of his tail
So he made one more hat And with one on each end
He went for a stroll in the heat
When a sparrow flew by
Saw Wendell and cried
'Meat and two veg., what a treat!'

THE JELLY FISH

If I had the choice to be
Anything on land or sea
The one thing that I wouldn't wish
To be's a lady jelly fish

No tingle could run down my spine
When his thousand eyes met mine
Nothing could be less romantic
Hanging round in the Atlantic
The one thing that I wouldn't wish
To be's a lady jelly fish

Who could say his heart was true
When I'd had a see-through view
How could one trip the light fantastic
With a plate made of elastic
If I had the choice to be
Anything on land or sea
The one thing that I wouldn't wish
To be's a lady jelly fish

No finger to admire a ring
No songs of love to hear or sing
No feet for handsome Prince's slippers
Breakfast entertaining kippers
And what about a million daughters
Marrying in foreign waters?
Oh no it's very clear to me
If I had the choice to be
Anything on land or sea
The one thing that I wouldn't wish
To be's a lady jelly fish.

CANDLE TANGO **

Jack a handsome Gypsy Moth
Wrapped his cloak around him
He wasn't cold, just sad that's all
For true love hadn't found him
Then on the midnight's Summer breeze
He heard the word 'amazing'
And saw a bent and aged Moth
Into a mothball gazing

The aged Moth looked up at him
Her eyes a faded yellow
And said, 'I've been expecting you'
'My young and handsome fellow.'
'In this mothball made of crystal'
'All the past and future's clear'
'I knew before the moon had risen'
'That I'd find you here'

'Should you need proof more conclusive'
'Your home's in a roll of cloth'
'Forty yards of tweed remaining'
'All the rest you've nibbled off
Handsome Jack could scarce believe it
But of course he had no choice
Said the old one, 'ask a question'
'When you've found your voice'

Said Jack, 'it's true love that I'm seeking'
'Is there someone there for me?'
Said the aged one, 'sit down dear'
'And I'll look and see'
'Oh my word, it's rather misty'
'I'll just clean it with this cloth'
'Look at that, would you believe it'
'A young and lovely lady Moth'

'I see you standing there beside her'
'Not a word does either say'
'And now a violin is playing'
'Gypsy music far away'
'On a table there's a candle'
'Polished oak reflects the light'
'I see you dancing to the music'
'In your arms you hold her tight'

'Now the music's getting louder'
'And the candle brighter too'
'In each other's eyes a gazing'
'Oh that I were young like you'
'On the wall I see two shadows'
'As you tango to and fro'
'One too near the flame that flickers'
'No,' said handsome Jack, 'please no'

'Tell me that she's in no danger'
'As our shadows dance the walls'
'In my crystal,' said the gazer
'As I look one shadow falls'
Said handsome Jack, 'I hope it's me then'
'For it surely must be better'
'To have danced the Candle Tango'
'Than never to have met her.'

'When I said I saw one falling'
'I meant of course.' the Moth replied
'Falling as in love quite madly'
'And not that one had died'
Said Handsome Jack, 'when will I meet her?'
'Tell me that we'll not be parted'
Said the Gypsy, 'that's the future'
'But the violins have started.'

DADDY LONG LEGS **

In the1ast rays of the sun
A daddy long legs flew
And though his life was nearly done
He felt as good as new
But to him it seemed a shame
That he'd soon disappear
Without one single claim to fame
To show that he'd been here

And so he drifted on the breeze
And he'd not gone too far
When he was sucked into the ventilator
Of a cinema
And there upon the silver screen
A dancing man appeared
In top hat, white tie, tails and cane
And everybody cheered
Then up into the beam of light
The daddy long legs flew
And on the silver screen his shadow
Started dancing too

Daddy Long Legs, dancing to the beat
Daddy Long Legs, two people, eight feet

As the man in tails tapped out each step,
Daddy Long Legs danced as well
Until somebody swatted him
And to the ground he fell
And as he lay there fading fast
He said, 'what do I care'
'I'm the only Daddy Long Legs'
'To have danced with Fred Astaire'.

Daddy Long Legs, dancing to the beat
Daddy Long Legs, two people, eight feet

FRED AND MARGUERITE **

Fred a little cockney sparrow
Looking cold and pale
Sleeping on a London roof
Fell off in a gale
He flapped his wings with all his might
But didn't stand a chance
And long before his breakfast time
He found himself in France

He landed in the Bois Boulougne
And gazed around unsure
Until a lady sparrow
Walked up and said 'bonjour'
'As you are a stranger here'
'I'll show you my Paree'
'Would you like to promenade?'
Said Fred, 'the answer's oui'

And as they flew across the town
The lady sparrow sang
And as she did her youthful voice
Across the rooftops rang
'Below us is the Champs Eleysees'
'Where I've often dined'
'Oh wouldn't it be nice'
'To have a lover who was kind'

'Over there the Tour d'Eiffel'
'Oh wouldn't it be sweet'
'To stand together at the top'
'With Paris at our feet'
'Accordions are playing in Monmartre'
'For that's my home'

'That broken rooftop's where I live'
'What's more I live alone'

'Down there is the Louvre Museum'
'All the finest art'
The moment that I saw your face'
'I knew I'd lost my heart'
'The bells you hear'
'That's Notre Dame'
'A wedding there is best'
'And there's a disused chimney pot'
'To build a double nest'

'I think I get your drift' said Fred
'It's lucky that I'm free'
'The moment I set eyes on you'
'I knew you were for me'
So they found a small café
In a cobbled street
He told her that his name was Fred
She said, 'mine's Marguerite'
She said, 'the memory of our day'
'Is one I'll always keep'
And after taking bread and wine
The sparrows fell asleep

He woke up to the sound of bells
And said, 'those bells I know'
'Those ain't the bells of Notre Dame'
'Them there's the Bells of Bow'
It's just another sparrow's dream
Above a London street
But I'll remember all my life
A bird called Marguerite.

FANSHAW THE FLY **

Fanshaw the Fly kept a very keen eye
On the overall World situation
And travelled by train in the hope that he'd gain
From the papers he read, information

He found that the Times was read on most lines
That led in and out of the City
And he'd stand and peruse the crosswords and clues
Saying, 'no, nearly right, what a pity'

Flies that he met were amazed he could get
All the things that he knew in his head
Yet it seemed that his brain was under no strain
'Pity more flies aren't like me,' he said

Then a friend said, 'some are, look I travel by car'
'To a library not far away'
'There's dozens of flies and here's the surprise
'They stand and read papers all day'

Said Fanshaw, 'take me, for this I must see'
'A meeting of mind's what I seek'
So he joined the throng but not for too long
For the fly paper's changed twice a week

ENGLEBERT THE ELECTRIC EEL

Englebert the electric eel
was handsome, young and single
And keen to find a lady eel
who'd make his senses tingle

But he's a problem hard to cure
for when he goes out dating
The girls he meets are all direct
whilst he is alternating

And every girl that he takes out
he very quickly loses
For when he kisses them goodnight
they always blow their fuses.

And so he found some rubber hose
and wriggled up inside
And with just his nose protruding,
went to find a bride

He found one and proposed to her,
they're getting married soon
She's no idea the shock she'll get,
on her honeymoon.

HELEN THE HIPPO **

Helen the Hippo was thrilled as could be
For tonight was her very first date
And so were her family, for single was she
And 92 stone over weight

Cried Helen, 'he's handsome, he's asked me to dine'
'At 9 o'clock round at his place',
And cleaning her teeth on a half submerged tree
She puts lots of hot mud on her face

Said her Mother, 'dear Helen, just where did you meet?'
'And did he remark on your size?'
Said her daughter, 'whilst swimming and all he could see'
'Was my nose and my ears and my eyes'

'I fell in love with his splendid moustache'
'All plastered down with red mud'
'He fell in love with the parts he could see'
'And told me his first name was Dud'

Said her Father, 'I think you should go for a run'
'You really should lose a few stone'
'Just fifteen or twenty could make all the difference'
'To marriage or living alone'

Poor Helen went running with tears in her eyes
The blazing hot sun on her back
But after ten miles she was still the same size
And her mud pack had started to crack

Like a large melting jelly she ran with a wobble
Another ten miles and she started to hobble
Wondering why she'd taken the trouble
For her chins were still treble, no sign of a double

Poor Helen just wept in the shade of a tree
For she knew that she'd never be lean
Then she heard the loud thunder of feet running by
It was Dudley all covered in steam

His splendid moustache drooped down to his knees
As did his stomach and chin
Then he slid to a halt and gasped with a wheeze
'It's no good I'll never be thin',

'Who'd want a lover who's quite so outsize?'
Said Helen, 'did somebody call?'
'And now we're together, the size of your thighs'
'Makes mine by comparison small'

Now they are married and happy as mud
With a big grown-up daughter called Kate
Who's got no idea with parents that size
That she's 92 stone over weight.

DOREEN THE DUCKLING *

Doreen was an ugly Duckling
Albert was a Royal Swan
Doreen took one look at Albert
and her heart was gone

But as she gazed at her reflection
In a puddle in the rain
From every angle and direction
The answer was the same

She was plain as he was handsome.
Forget the curtsey she'd rehearsed
So Doreen ran down to the river
And jumped in it headfirst

And on the swift green shining water
Albert drifted by quite near
His head beneath his wing
A-dreaming, heading for the weir

She paddles wildly, wings a-flapping
Well below the danger sign
Her shouts above the roaring waters
Woke him just in time

And as she'd risked her life to save him
And he saw her heart was true
He asked her if she was still single
And if so, would he do?

Alas, she said, I fear I'm ugly
Plain at best, if anything
And so he placed upon her finger
His gold signet ring

Then he said should you but treasure
All things pleasing to the eye
Then of life you'll have no measure
And beauty will pass by

For beauty comes all shapes and sizes
All God's creatures great and small
And he cleverly devises
Different faces for us all

As you see me now I'm handsome
Some day I'll be old and fat
Nothing's worth a Prince's ransom
To marry just for that.

STANLEY THE STORK **

Stanley the Stork went for a walk
In a Park and then paused by a puddle
As a girl and a man who were pushing a pram
Stopped for a kiss and a cuddle

The baby inside, dropped its rattle and cried
For the loss seemed to make it unhappy
Then it stood up and peered and as Stanley had feared
Fell out of the pram in its nappy

The couple strolled on, unaware it had gone
Young Stanley could hardly believe it
So, Stanley the Stork abandoned his walk
And decided to try and retrieve it

By the time he had picked up the bundle and looked
The couple with pram had departed
So up Stanley flew for an aerial view
And that's how the rumour got started

Two elderly spinsters saw Stanley fly down
To the pram and put baby back in it
Said one to the other, 'that chap kissed her twice'
'There'll be another one down in a minute'.

WICKED MCNAUGHT

There's a terrible tale that's told
Of a castle in the Glen
Haunted by McNaught of Naughton
The wickedest of men.

He died whilst fighting twenty soldiers
Single-handed twelve he slew
Until a razor-edged Claymore
Cut his strong right leg in two

Now from the crypt and full red-bearded
Every night at the stroke of ten
he hops out looking for his lost leg
That's said to roam the glen.

Passing travellers swear they've seen it
Hopping round the castle grounds
With McNaught whose close behind it
As it jumps in leaps and bounds

He tries with might and main to catch it
But it stays one jump ahead
And screaming like a man demented
He beats his big fists on his head

And cries, 'I curse the curse I'm cursed with'
'How can I do evil work'
'When the tartan sock I'm chasing's'
'Where I keep my little dirk'

Along the battlements down stairwells
Through the big hall, servant's quarters
Then the chase across the drawbridge
Mirrored in the moat's dark waters

To that battleground so fatal
To the spot where he was slain
There he grabs it by the ankle
And sticks it on again

Then with an evil roar of triumph
He cries, 'my missing leg I've found'
And then a voice calls out from Heaven
It's on the wrong way round.

CAMILLE THE SEAL **

My name is Camille
I'm a small baby seal
And I'm sure that you're happy to know
That my fur coat's so warm
I can get up at dawn
And play all day long in the snow

Well today, when at play
With my young brother, Sam
We met a strange creature
Which Mother called man
She cried out 'beware'
'And please don't go near'
But we were so young
That we didn't know fear

So I showed him my slide
Which I made yesterday
And my brother and I
Said 'do come and play'
But it seemed that the man
Didn't quite understand
For he raised something long,
Cold and sharp in his hand,

And then Sam went to sleep
Though he wasn't in bed
And I called for Mother
'It's too late she said'

But I'm sure that you're happy to know
My fur coat's so warm
You can get up at dawn
And play all day long in the snow.

KENNY THE KOALA **

Kenny is a Koala Bear his nose is always red
Every morning he sleeps late he can't get out of bed
And just like every Koala bear he doesn't walk he weaves
For his diets alcoholic Eucalyptus leaves

And as it's always opening time, he doesn't have to wait
He has a double when he wakes just to put him straight

Once he fell out of a tree into a passing truck
And said 'that's clumsy, silly me,
what bloomin' awful luck'
But still I reckon it's a tale I can always brag on
I'll be the only Koala bear to end up on the wagon.

OLIVER THE OCTOPUS

Oliver the Octopus,
with eyes as big as plates
Sits in his underwater cave
And waits and waits and waits

He lives just off the Isle of Mull
Where soft backed crabs are plenty
But it's not food he's waiting for
You see his life is empty

There is no lady Octopus
To share his cares and woes
The reason is that Oliver
Can't see beyond his nose

Short sighted to the Nth degree,
On touch alone reliant
He searches with his tentacles
All long and strong and pliant

Just above this hidey hole
So dark and deep and cold
There rose a cliff and on its brow
A kilted piper strolled

A sad lament snatched by the wind
Upon his pipes he played
Then upon a stone he slipped
Threw up his arms and swayed

And like a tartan windmill
He wobbled to and fro
And gazed with horror as his bagpipes
Vanished down below

They sank and landed by the cave
A tentacle soon found them
And then another two or three
Which wrapped them selves around them

And then they disappeared inside
Now Oliver's delighted
It's amazing how true love can last
When you really are shortsighted.

TEDDY'S TEA TIME **

A Teddy Bear sits on a mattress
One glass eye and threadbare paw
Looking at a Cuckoo clock
Which tells it's nearly ten to four

Four o'clock is Teddy's teatime
Lots of friends and fancy cake
Although it's only pretend eating
Oh how long ten minutes take.

Shadows grow on distant hillside
Orange sun on glassy sea,
All in his amber eye reflected
And still ten minutes left 'til tea,

The mattress striped is old and broken.
Rusty springs through stuffing show
The Cuckoo clock is also broken
But how's a Teddy s'posed to know

Unaware he's been abandoned,
That this is not the nursery cot
The hills and sea just glass, old papers
On a disused rubbish plot.

A telephone that no-one answers
Empty tins that once held tea
The clock that still says nearly tea-time,
Where can all the children be

For ages now he's lain unwanted
Saluting with a threadbare paw
He'll never know how he's been discarded
Until the clock reads after four

Don't tell him that the clock is broken,
As long as Teddy doesn't know,
It will always soon be tea time
As it was so long ago.

CAPTAIN BEAKY'S PANTOMIME **

It's Christmas time throughout the land
And Captain Beaky and his Band
That's Timid Toad and Reckless Rat,
Artful Owl and Batty Bat
Are painting a big cardboard sign that reads
The 'WUDLAND PANTOMIME'

In my mind, said Captain Beaky,
'There isn't any question'
'My name should be above the title
As it was my suggestion'
'Hold on a minute' there', said Bat,
'This piece of cardboard's mine'
'But only I, said Artful Owl,
'Can spell pantomime'

'That's very true', said Timid Toad,'
And he spelt Wudland too'
Said Rat,'well Wudland looks all wrong,
There should be one more U'
'Let's not argue now', said Owl,
'The play's the thing to plan'
'I favour Humpty Dumpty
Or even Peter Pan'

'We haven't got a Crocodile,
Or clock', said Reckless Rat
Said Bat,' we could do Cinderella,
I bet we all know that'
Said Artful Owl, 'he's right of course,
I fear the point had missed us'
'With Rat and Bat to play the parts,
we've got the ugly sisters'

'Timid Toad, of course,
Can play the part of Cinderella'
Said Beaky, 'Bags I play the Prince,
That handsome, charming feller'
Agreed', said Owl, 'of course you'll need
Me as your acting tutor'

Said Reckless Rat, 'Ow would you like
A quick punch up the hooter?'
Bat and me's not playing parts
Unless they're ones we've chosen'
Said Timid Toad, 'please lets decide,
My feet are getting frozen'

Said Captain Beaky, 'that's it Toad,
We don't have to think twice'
And under WUDLAND PANTOMIME,
He wrote the words ON ICE.
At that moment Sid the Snake
Swung down from a tree
And hissed in Captain Beaky's ear,
'Hiss there a part for me?'

And then he went on to explain
He wasn't really bad
And when you're lonely and unloved,
At Christmas time it's sad
Well l can't see why not', said Owl,
'But can you dance and sing?'
'I can hiss', said Hissing Sid.
Said Owl, 'right, Demon King!'

And so they all did pantomime,
skating on a pond
And Hissing Sid played Demon King,
The Beanstalk and a wand.
Dick Whittington was played by Owl,
He painted all the signs
And Timid Toad picked Sleeping Beauty
'Cause he can't remember lines.

Bat and Rat were ugly sisters,
The kind you love to hate
But Beaky, dressed as handsome Prince
Found he couldn't skate
So by the cardboard sign he stood,
A paintbrush in his hand
And over PANTOMIME he wrote
BY CAPTAIN BEAKY's BAND

And as the Demon King got cheers
For everything he did
He added on in smaller letters,
GUEST STAR HISSING SID.

CAPTAIN BEAKY'S
CHRISTMAS CAROL **

Captain Beaky and his Band
Will soon be carol singing
With their lanterns and their candles
They'll be doorbell ringing
For the song that Owl has written
And it's all in rhyme
Tells of their hopes of happiness
For all at Christmastime

We are Captain Beaky's Band,
This is our Christmas song
We wish you all a Merry Christmas
And a life that's long

With lots of food and things to eat
And parties to go to
And if you live alone
We hope someone takes care of you
And to all those little children
Who write to Santa Claus
We hope the presents that we get
Are just as good as yours

To all of you both young and old
We hope you'll never cease
To make this world a better place
To bring us lasting peace
For after all we all live here
All colours and all creeds
And if we'd share I'm sure we'd
Have enough for all our needs

So remember Christmas time
And if someone is in need
Be like Captain Beaky's Band
And do them a good deed.

Goodbye from Rat, Toad, Owl and Bat
And Captain Beaky too
We're going to have a Merry Christmas
We hope you have one too

MANDY THE MOUSE **

A youthful mole on night patrol
Has just made this report
He spotted Hissing Sid last night
And though his eyesight's short
He swears that Sid had slithered by
With mischief on his mind
So pulling down his moleskin hat
He'd followed close behind

And there in woodlands darkest dell
Sid stopped a mouse called Mandy
Then tied her up with her own tail
And stole her box of candy
Then swayed about before her eyes
And sang a haunting tune
And claimed his power to hypnotise
Would make her sleep 'till noon

But half way through the second verse
The mole's brain went all numb
And falling backwards in a trance
He slept 'till half past one
He woke and freed the lady mouse
Still tied up to the tree
Who hummed a rather haunting tune
As she went home for tea

O'FLANAGAN THE BEETLE

O' Flanagan an Irish Beetle
On a building site
Sat in the shadow of a brick
And pondered on his plight

He'd taken up religion
Of a quite unusual kind
And wore a little Dhoti
That just covered his behind...

The mystic East attracted him
He hoped to go there later
To find out why the world was built
And who was it's creator ...

Just then the earth about him shook
The skyline rose and fell
And pillars of iron and stone appeared
And O 'Flanagan gave a yell

For high in the sky there hung a sign
And clutching his Dhoti skimpy
He knew God's name
And who'd made the world
Good heavens he said
It's Wimpey!

THE WATER BOATMAN

On any village pond you'll find
On a summers day
Water boatmen rowing there
To pass the time away
And there's a tale that they tell
And many swear it's true
The day a water beetle came
And formed a rowing crew

I need eight lads the beetle cried
The fittest and the best
To scull with skill
Across the pond much faster than the rest.
Believe me sir, a boatman said,
Though rowing's quite an art
I've got some lads who row so quick
They arrives before they start

That's good to hear the beetle said.
Now there's my rival's craft
Eight acorns glued together
Oh how the boatmen laughed
And then they saw the strangest sight
For wearing shorts and caps
Grasshoppers eight in number came
And called out "Hello chaps

We've just hopped down from Cambridge
We're mad keen rowing blues
And every bet to date we've won
In fact we've yet to lose"
And jumping in the acorn boat
They set off at a lick
My word the water boatman said
That's pretty blooming quick!

Come me on lads all get in line
We'll show 'em what we've got
And bending their long slender arms
Across the pond they shot
In and out the beetle cried
Much faster number four
We're flat out now the boatman said
And we ain't got no more

So round and round the pond they rowed
Until the day was done
And then the water boatmen said
We've had it lads they've won!
Hooray cried the Cambridge crew
We've still not lost a bet
It's time we all hopped home again
Our feet are frightfully wet.

I'm not surprised the boatman said
Them Cambridge Chaps is rotten
That acorn boat's got holes in
They was running on the bottom
'Twas most unfair and by that count
We're still the fastest crew
But doesn't it just show
What education does for you!

BIOGRAPHIES

Keith Michell
(Actor / Artist)

Better known as an Actor, Playwright and Director, Keith Michell turned his artistic hand to providing all the illustrations for the original two Jeremy Lloyd Captain Beaky books as well as the designs for the BBC TV and West End Shows.

He also found time as an actor to narrate the adventures of Captain Beaky and Hissing Sid on records and television, and found himself in the unlikely position of appearing on BBC TV's Top of the Pops performing Captain Beaky which went into the charts at no 2.

Keith Michell who in his main role as an actor has starred in many plays, in London and on Broadway. He has also appeared at Stratford and the Old Vic and has starred in musicals, including *Irma La Dodce, Robert and Elizabeth* and *On The 20th Century*, in his many roles in films and television he is, perhaps best known for his role as Henry VIII in the BBC television series *The Six Wives Of Henry VIII*. He has made recordings and has held several exhibitions of his paintings. A former artistic director of Chichester Festival Theatre he combined his talents, directing and designing *Twelfth Night*. Keith recently visited Australia where in addition to a series of concerts of his 'one man show' he was invited to appear with the Melbourne Theatre Company in his own play *'Pete McGynty'*.

Jim Parker
(Composer / Co-Producer)

You may have caught the name Jim Parker as the credits of a TV Series have rolled by. Among the 100 or more shows he has scored include "The House of Elliott", "Moll Flanders", "A Rather English Marriage", "House of Cards", "Dirty Tricks." His album work includes, the Sir John Betjeman Albums 'Banana Blush' and 'Late Flowering Love, 'Captain Beaky and His Band' albums. Concert works have been written for The Nash Ensemble, Philip Jones Brass, The Hilliard Ensemble, The Albion Ensemble and the Wallace Collection among others. He also has an honorary degree from the Guildhall School of Music and Drama

Hugh Murphy
(Producer)

Hugh Murphy as a producer had an eclectic background, working originally as an assistant with Shel Talmy who produced the Kinks, The Who, Manfred Mann, Easy Beats, Pentangle.

Hugh went on to produce the Kursaal Flyers, Kilburn and the High Roads (Ian Dury), String Driven Thing, Gary Shearston (*"I Get A Kick Out Of You"*), Shepstone and Dibbens (*"Shady Lady"*), Dana (*"Please Tell Him I Said Hello"*), the two Sir John Betjeman albums, Scouse the Mouse, and Gerry Rafferty's *"Baker Street"* among many, many others. Hugh produced the first Captain Beaky album (Captain Beaky Volume I).

* Captain Beaky and His Band Volume I
Features: The King's Singers, Jeremy Lloyd,
Keith Michell, Harry Secombe, Peter Sellers
and Twiggy.

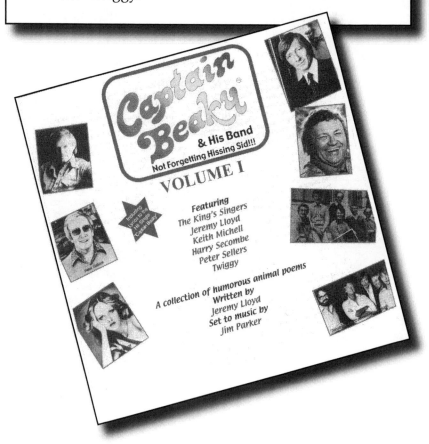

** Captain Beaky and His Band Volume II
Features: Petula Clark, Noel Edmonds,
Penelope Keith, The King's Singers, Jeremy
Lloyd, Keith Michell, Harry Secombe, Peter
Skellern, St. Paul's Choristers.

Both CDs are available through
www.captainbeaky.com